A Teacher, Carol

Burnt-out Educator Rediscovers Her Spirit!

By Ricki Stein, Heather Harlen, Vicky Lynott and Audrey Nolte

National Writing Project / Penn State Lehigh Valley Writing Project Fellows

Foreword

"**W**e need to write a book. That's what's missing!"
After 12 years working with Lehigh Valley Writing Project Summer Youth Camps, I was ready to tackle a book that represented the Penn State site.

I sat down to pitch the idea to Nancy Coco, LVWP Director. The security guard knocked on her office door. Out of thin air, Nancy said, "I'm meeting with our Writer-in-Residence." Haha! What a title! What a responsibility!

At conferences, "experts" tell us how to do our jobs as teachers. But aren't we all experts? We're in the trenches every day and we know how to reach our students. When we struggle, we look for ideas from others. I wanted to collaborate on a book with other Fellows to hammer home the fact that we are, collectively, experts. I wanted to share the strength of our diverse teaching and writing backgrounds to promote the value of the National Writing Project's model of teachers teaching teachers. We should be proud of our qualifications and expertise. We need to recognize ourselves as the experts we truly are.

"I don't want to write just another teacher book," I told the initial gathering of 12 Fellows. "We are going to challenge ourselves by writing realistic fiction." I wanted a short, fast-paced read for busy teachers. I wanted to inspire teachers to write. I wanted to inspire teachers to collaborate.

After asking who felt comfortable committing to the book's format and timeline, Heather Harlen, Vicky Lynott and Audrey Nolte stepped up to the plate. To make progress, we knew we needed a structure in order to divide and conquer. Heather came up with the idea of following the template of Charles Dickens' *A Christmas Carol*. Everybody picked a ghost and we were off and writing. The first drafts proved painful because we all wrote too much. We set word-number limits. We learned to "kill our darlings," keeping in mind Mark Twain's counsel that "what you leave out is as important as what you keep in." Surprisingly, the process became the most fun during revision when we all worked together, wordsmithing every sentence.

Our characters became real, they drove the plot and we visited our own ghosts of teaching past, present and future. Now that we're on a roll, we're ready to write the sequel in what we hope will become a series. It is our hope you recognize yourselves and can identify with the concepts.

Ricki Stein
Writer-in-Residence
Penn State Lehigh Valley Writing Project

Acknowledgements

We offer gratitude to....

Nancy Coco, Director of the Penn State Lehigh Valley Writing Project, for giving us the go-ahead and for support of this project.

MJ Kelly, Anthony Fredericks and Nancy Coco for reading our first draft and offering valuable feedback.

Randy Bernhard, Ricki's husband, for surrendering his kitchen and delaying his roofing project for the sake of the writing process.

Nicole Pappas for her precise proofreading skills.

Joy Nelson for her cover design.

Mark Swartz for his page layout skills.

Our families, friends and colleagues for their support.

Chapter 1
Homeroom

Slouched in front of her computer deleting emails, Carol Cosgroe knew she should just shut down the laptop and go home. After all, it was 3 o'clock Friday afternoon. At the end of a long school week in her seventh grade classroom, the clutter of shoebox dioramas overwhelmed her.

Jamie Ardiente breezed in like a whirling dervish, her long, brown curls springing in time to her step. Her red skirt swirled around her legs. One of Carol's team teaching partners, the 27-year-old Jamie still brought the fire every day to her classroom. Students loved her fashionable outfits, dangly earrings and necklaces. Loved the reggaeton music she played. Loved the animated antics as she talked with her hands, bracelets bouncing as she danced around the room during science lessons. Basically, kids loved her youthful energy. By comparison, Carol felt like a slug. She couldn't believe just two years earlier she had mentored Jamie and matched her enthusiasm.

"Hey, Girl!" Jamie started, clapping her hands and arching her eyebrows above her polka-dot glasses. Carol looked up. "A bunch of us are going to the new IMAX theater to see *Rescue*. Come with us. We'll hit happy hour after."

Carol rolled her eyes in disgust, tucked a gray strand of hair behind her ear and turned back to her laptop. She deleted an email about another hoagie fundraiser and muttered, "Bah, humbug."

"You know me!" Jamie pressed on. "I like to be there opening night! Half price drink specials at Fezziwig's Tavern after!"

"I have to get home," Carol sighed with exhaustion. "Sara has dance class. Timmy has physical therapy for his leg."

"TGIF, Carol! It's happy hour!"

"Gimme a break. It's happy for single, young women like you," Carol nearly spat. "I'm happy for you. But I have obligations. Don't worry about me."

"But come on! Look at this flyer for the movie!" Jamie sang, waving the paper toward Carol. "Fezziwig's has those appletinis I know you love. We have a three-day weekend. Everyone needs a break."

"You are persistent, Jamie! If this teaching gig doesn't work out, you could always be a lawyer. You could even chase ambulances."

"Nah, teaching's my niche," Jamie said. "I like being the queen of my OWN court! Anyway, can't your husband take the kids where they need to go? I thought this marriage thing was 50/50?"

"HA! Maybe it's a good thing you don't have a steady boyfriend. If I were young and single, maybe I'd go out, but I have other responsibilities."

Jamie raised her hands over her head, pointing her fingers to opposite sides of the room like a flight attendant. In a nasally voice, she broadcast, "Be sure to adjust your oxygen mask before helping others."

"I'm heading home for an emergency landing, honey. I'll see you Tuesday. Have fun."

"Suit yourself. Try to have a good weekend!" Jamie called, practically skipping out of the room.

Mumbling to herself, Carol said, "I wish I still had that kind of energy. Do I stay home for a mental health day or spend more time developing lesson plans a robot could follow? I need to recharge my batteries. The question is, HOW?"

Talking out loud to herself, she grumbled, "If only non-teachers could understand my job is so much more than 7 to 3 with summers off. How about the planning, the correcting, the reading, the bulletin boards? How about all the overwhelming and demanding daily hours after 3 p.m. and on the weekends? Heck, we cram 365 days of work into 180!"

Before shutting down her computer, Carol checked her email one more time. Even though she had just deleted an email about a hoagie fundraiser, there flashed a new email subject line in bold face: "Lacking energy? Read this."

"Yikes," Carol thought. "It read my mind." She hit delete.

With that, another email popped in. "Need some reminders of how life used to be fun?"

"CREEEEPY!" Carol sang. She hit delete.

With that, another email popped in. "Beware the visions of your past."

"What the hell?" Carol yelled. "DELETE!"

Another email popped in: "Go home. We'll come visit!"

"AAAAGGGHHHH!" Carol screamed. "I'm so tired I'm dreaming."

She pushed back her chair and stood up. Carol reached down to grab her teacher bag from the floor and flopped it on her desk. Scanning the desktop surface, she decided what else she needed to stuff into her bag for weekend homework. "Better not forget the manila folder full of papers to grade," she sighed as she shoved it in her bag. She grabbed her gradebook and added it. "Don't forget the red pen!" Carol snarled to herself.

Carol turned back to the laptop, her mood completely fouled. She leaned over and typed an email to her husband, reminding him to finish cleaning the basement closet before she got home. No "xoxox," no "I Love You," just a short, clipped sentence. She slammed the laptop lid down, yanked out the power cord and wrapped it up. Shoving it all in her bag, Carol grabbed her coat off the back of her chair and stomped toward the door.

"Appletinis! Who needs appletinis when I can enjoy myself grading student papers?" After picking up the paper balls from the floor, pushing in the chairs, lining up the desks and switching off the lights, Carol locked the door and headed for her family taxi, aka the van.

Chapter 2
First Period

On the drive home, Carol listened to the radio and despite the mellow music, her shoulders still hunched up by her ears. Enya sang "sail away, sail away, sail away" on the radio. Still, Carol gripped the steering wheel for the entire ride. She pulled into the driveway and dragged herself into the kitchen. Bob bumped around boxes and whistled in the basement. She went to the top of the stairs, opened the door and called down, "Hi Bob. Done yet?"

"Almost! Glad you're home!" Bob called.

Carol glanced at the clock. Thirty minutes before she needed to get Sara to dance class and Timmy to the physical therapist. She poured herself a glass of water, slumped down in a kitchen chair, elbows on the table, jaw hunkered between her hands. The silence engulfed her, until her phone vibrated with a text message. It was Jamie, inviting her, again, to Fezziwig's. Carol typed back, "Tempting, but rather enjoying my personal little pity party. No worries. Will find a way to recharge my batteries."

She caught her reflection in the sliding glass door. Carol suddenly realized that twenty years in the trenches had passed so quickly. Although she felt the same, the mirror didn't lie. Her flecks of blond highlights muted the gray strands in her funky short hair. Carol's body had rounded through her thirties. She strove to find ways to camouflage with decorative scarves or jewelry. Who was she kidding? Although bottles and tubes of the next miracle cures littered her bathroom counter, nothing could mask the acne and wrinkles breeding on her face.

"What does Jamie see when *she* looks in the mirror?" Carol wondered. "Does she question herself as much as I do? Questions ... hmmm ... I still ask good questions."

Next to Jamie's confident dancing bling, Carol's expert

ability to form questions brought students to higher-level thinking. Carol remembered reading *The Sweetest Fig* by Chris Van Allsburg with her reading remediation students and asking them about types of dreams. During that lesson, students often remarked that a wish is a kind of a dream.

Carol only had dark bedtime dreams now. The inspirational, motivational dreams were gone.

"Wish ... dream ... words that mean the same thing," Carol thought. The jargon of her profession rattled against her brain. Bloom's taxonomy ... DOK ... PSSA ... UBD ... SIG... learning targets ... standards ... SBG … Common Core ... essential questions ... benchmark assessments ... NCLB ... 4sights ... Study Island ... SAT ... Keystones ...

When did the sounds of these words obliterate the students? Carol used to love the art more than the science of teaching. Too often she felt alone in the trenches, surrounded by politics.

She became a teacher to link kids to the world. Her middle school position as a social studies and language arts teacher allowed her to provide a concrete foundation of background knowledge. Plus, she could easily integrate writing into her curriculum. How could she maintain an anchor to what she intuitively knew worked while incorporating 21st century skills for balance?

As Sara and Timmy slammed doors upstairs, Carol thought, "How can I be revolutionary when I am teaching to the test? How can I have kids become activists when I am struggling to become alive? I used to be a teacher of the heart, but somehow I've lost my own heart." Her dehydrated motivation and search for inspiration led to the perfect storm of absolute isolation. Carol's well was dry.

Zoning out, she stared at the microwave door. In the window she detected a reflection. Thinking she was hallucinating, she grabbed her trifocals off the table to focus. It looked like a face from the past. She froze. Suddenly, she heard the unmistakable "swish, swish, swish" of pantyhose rubbing together, from one leg to the other.

"Sounds like Marlee," Carol said looking up. "That can't be her. She's on sabbatical in Costa Rica."

For 13 years, Carol and Marlee Jacobs had taught together on a middle school team. When Carol decided to teach in another school district, the two teaching partners hugged and cried.

BANG! Thump! Smoke poofed out from Marlee's ankles. There she stood on Carol's kitchen floor, in person. Or so it appeared.

"Hey, Partner! What's goin' on?" Marlee bellowed, her usual come-in-the-door announcement. Carol cocked her head and squinted.

Wearing a rock-climbing harness over hiking shorts, pantyhose, camp shirt and boots, Marlee carried a clear Lucite container. "Why are you looking so gloomy?"

"Marlee! What are you doing here?" Carol asked, snapping out of her reverie and feeling a goose bump chill.

"A little birdie told me my pal needed a pep talk," Marlee responded loudly, her Mickey Mouse earrings swinging wildly. Placing the container gently in front of Carol, Marlee added, "Here. A little chocolate therapy might help!"

On the clear container, seventh grader Emily Spain had written in marker, "Mrs. Cosgroe's Jar of Sanity." She had filled it with Hershey Kisses. After eating many of that first batch of Kisses by herself, Carol buried the jar in Marlee's classroom closet. They took it out when they needed to get past frustrations or the day's usual challenges.

"Haha! Haven't seen these Hershey Kisses in a while," Carol said.

"Remember the student who gave us this gift?" Marlee asked, fluffing her short curly hair and throwing her arms up in victory. "That's the ticket. Remember the students. Remember the students. Remember the students!!!!"

"Hey, knock it off, Marlee. I hear you putting too many

exclamation points at the end of that sentence! You are only allowed ONE!" Carol told her.

"Remember how you were thrilled Emily started putting punctuation *in* her writing? Remember how you got her to write full sentences?"

"Yes, I do," Carol said. "Tape recorder. But what are you doing here? Are you real? Let me touch you to see if you are real." Carol timidly stood up from her chair, inched over and leaned toward Marlee. She touched Marlee on the upper arm. "Hey, this sabbatical is doing you some good. Those biceps are feeling firm. What are you doing with yourself these days?"

Marlee struck a body-builder pose. She laughed out loud. "Ha ha ha! Well, I'm taking rock-climbing classes, working out. Costa Rica and the rain forest are awesome. I needed a mental pick-me-up. After you left the district, I felt like I was just pushing students through like the administrative paperwork I found in my mailbox every day. I was prepping them for the state tests in a mechanical way. I wasn't helping the kids the way they needed help. You know I love the scientific method, but the assessment data collection needed no hypothesizing. I needed a break. I needed to reset my thinking so I could remember the students."

Creak. The basement door opened and Bob stepped into the kitchen. His eyebrows arched up in surprise. "Carol, are you OK? You look a little shell shocked. What's going on?"

"You don't see anybody here besides me?" Carol asked him.

"No. I heard you talking but there's no one here," Bob said, looking around. "I'm worried about you. How about if I take the kids to dance and PT and you can take a nap?"

Marlee laughed heartily, her whole body shaking up and down. Carol looked at Bob, who looked back at her. No reaction. Apparently he didn't hear anything.

"Ummm. Go ahead," Carol said, rubbing her temples and grimacing. She looked past Bob at the vision of Marlee. "I think I need some time to regroup. I appreciate the help. Supper will be ready when you come back."

"OK, we're off," Bob said, calling upstairs, "Let's go kids. We have places to go! I'll meet you in the car in five minutes."

Marlee pulled out a chair and joined Carol at the table. She reached into the container and helped herself to five Kisses, then pushed the jar away. "So, my friend, why the long face?"

Carol removed her reading glasses from her nose and put them on top of her head. Rubbing the red spots left behind on the tip of her nose, she stood up, stretched her arms and started pacing around the kitchen, talking with her hands. "Clearly I've lost my mind! You're not here. You're in Costa Rica. This must be my subconscious screaming out for help. Let's just go with it!"

"Well, I just feel like I'm not reaching the kids," Carol began. "I get them excited with these really great social studies projects and language arts writing prompts, or at least they seem like really great prompts. The kids get started on them, but they don't like to finish. Most of them refuse to do any school work at home. They really don't believe in meeting deadlines."

Marlee scooped out four more Hershey kisses. She pushed two of them to Carol and started peeling open one for herself.

Marlee asked, "Do you know what's going on at home with these kids? That's one reason you and I always worked so well together. We always thought about the kids and what baggage they brought to school. You can't forget that. It definitely gets in the way of their learning, and maybe especially in the way of their writing."

Carol pondered. She always credited Marlee's home life for her amazing ability to keep a keen eye on students' emotional and social needs. Marlee's son was a good natured kid with multiple disabilities. She and her husband knew his limitations but they never let him wallow in them. They pushed him to be the best he could be. That's how Marlee worked with kids at school, gently pushing them to their best work without taking "I can't" for any excuses.

"That's what I miss about working with you, Marlee," Carol said. "You always reminded me, 'We don't know what's going on at home.' I don't hear those reminders at my new school. Strong collegiality is missing. I feel so isolated."

Again, Marlee scooped out four more Hershey Kisses. She pushed two of them to Carol and started peeling one for herself.

"Well, here I am!" Marlee boomed. "I'm reminding you now!!!!!!!!!"

"You only get ONE exclamation point!"

Marlee picked up a Kiss. She held it up toward the light, pretending to examine it. She held it toward Carol. "So about Emily. Remember how you got her to put punctuation in her writing?"

Carol heard a faint pinging by the sink. She and Marlee looked over. Out of nowhere, a speech bubble appeared in the air, holding a picture of Carol and Emily, a redhead with plenty of freckles. They sat side by side, in classic writer's conference style, looking at Emily's writer's notebook. Carol pointed to two lines in the notebook and directed, "Emily, read this out loud."

As the speech bubble faded, Carol said to Marlee, "I gave her an old fashioned cassette tape recorder. She read her writing out loud to herself, listened back and could fix the sentences."

"See?" Marlee asked. "That was a success. You reached her."

"Yes," Carol said. She held up a Hershey Kiss and toasted, "To Emily and her Jar of Sanity!"

"Here, here!" Marlee agreed, holding aloft another foil wrapped treat.

Carol said, "But there was nothing wrong with Emily's home life. She was a lucky kid with great parents and an awesome sister. They really supported her and us."

"Yes, that's true," Marlee said. "Many of your current students are probably in a good situation, too. But kids are kids. It doesn't mean they like to do work and hand it in on time. They probably have other stuff to do after school, like babysitting, music lessons and baseball practice."

"Oh, I don't doubt that," Carol said. "But really, way too many of my students aren't handing in their work on time. Back in the day, kids met deadlines. I don't want them to fail. I know they can do the work. I'm giving them fun and relevant assignments."

"It's never about the assignment, my friend," Marlee said, adjusting ghostly spectacles on her nose. "It's always about the students. Where's your copy of this?"

Marlee reached into the back pocket of her shorts. With a flourish, she held up a tube of paper. With her right hand holding it at the top, she scrolled out the paper. Carol pulled her glasses from the top of her head and settled them on her nose to read:

One Hundred Years from Now

(*excerpt from "Within My Power" by Forest Witcraft*)

One hundred years from now
It will not matter
What kind of car I drove,
What kind of house I lived in,
How much money was in my bank account
Nor what my clothes looked like.
But the world may be a better place
because I was important in the life of a child.

"Well?" asked Marlee. "Where is yours? This was always our bible."

Carol crossed her arms over her chest and hung her head. "You're right."

Marlee stood up. "Let's take a little field trip," she said. She placed one hand under Carol's elbow to nudge her out of the chair. With her other hand, she scooped up the Lucite container, curled her forearm and secured it against her bulging bicep.

"Where are we going?" Carol asked as a vortex of dust swirled the two colleagues up and out of the kitchen and plunked them down in Carol's old classroom at their middle school.

"Wow! How... how... how'd you do that?" Carol stammered.

"I told you, I've been taking classes!" Marlee replied. "Turn around and let's take a look at these."

On Carol's old desk sat a pile of 15 yearbooks. "Wow. You saved all those?" Carol asked.

"It's about these," Marlee said, opening the cover of a yearbook to reveal student messages and signatures. "I always loved having kids sign my yearbook when they signed each other's. It gave me a yardstick to measure the impact I had on the kids."

Carol walked over and smoothed her hand down the stack of shiny books. She opened the cover of the book on top. The white pages on the left and right were covered with writing from students. She reached up to her head for her reading glasses and lowered them to the end of her nose. She read, *"Thanks for being there when I needed a friend, Traci."*

Carol read through several hand-written entries. She turned the page and found a folded piece of notebook paper stuck in the book. Opening the note, Carol scanned the words. *"You always know how to make someone feel good about themselfes and I apreshate that. Thank you for helping me through my problems. Jen."*

"Well, Carol said, "her sentiment was good. Spelling not so much!"

"She could spell just fine when she had to!" Marlee said.

Carol plopped into the desk chair, plunked her elbows on the desk and propped her jaw in her hands. "Times have changed. It doesn't seem the same."

Marlee stood in front of the white board at the front of the room. "Times have changed," she agreed. "We have to change with them, to some extent."

"Give me a Kiss and then give me a for-instance," Carol demanded.

Marlee placed the Lucite container on the desk, popped open the lid and scooped out four more Hershey Kisses. She slid two over to Carol and started unwrapping one for herself.

"For instance, kids still like to tell stories. Remember the tall tale unit?" Marlee asked as she flipped open the third yearbook down the pile and pointed to a boy's photo. "Paul was convinced he was a pro surfer, telling us and the kids quite an extensive story. At a parent conference, we told Paul's mom it was so awesome that he surfed! The mom was flabbergasted and assured us this was a fantasy she had not heard. After that, Paul developed a phobia and stopped coming to school. You and I helped him transition his way back in with a lot of patience and humor and suggestions about doing work in small doses. By the end of the school year he was back like nothing happened. The next year his mother and the guidance counselors assured us he was loving school and having a great year."

Carol sat up straight, the proverbial light bulb going off in her head. "It's such a natural for adolescents," she said. "Some of them tell so many tales, they don't know what's true anymore."

Marlee nodded. "You always told them to practice some short stories on their parents, and me, before they extended one in writing for language arts. I believed so many of them."

"Well, you always were pretty gullible," Carol assured. "Those stories are always fun!"

"That's my point, my friend," Marlee said. "Life's too short. Enjoy it now, and share that joy with students. Share your stories with them and the joy you find in writing. They'll come around. They'll get their work done."

"You were always a good woman of teaching, Marlee."

"Children are my business. I teach science, but truly, I teach students," Marlee said.

Carol squirmed in her chair. "I hear you, Marlee. But I need to learn something new about teaching, about how to inspire kids to want to do the work, the writing. I know I could get better results from them."

"Now you're talking," Marlee said. "We are life-long learners. Go learn something new. There must be a class that could help you help kids with their writing."

The two old friends sat quietly for a few minutes. Carol sat up, energized. "When I was a student teacher, my co-op teacher was really big on writing across the curriculum. And I vaguely remember something about the National Writing Project. A colleague of mine went through the Penn State Lehigh Valley Writing Project. Maybe I should talk to her."

"Definitely," Marlee said. "Let me know how it turns out. Right now, I gotta go. I've got a really cute rock climbing instructor waiting for me at La Piedra. Oooh, before I forget - did you get emails about visitors?"

"Ummm ... I thought they were spam, so I deleted them."

Marlee tightened her rock climbing harness and said, "Some spam is worth heeding. You will have three other visitors tonight."

"Visitors? My bathrooms aren't clean!"

Before Carol's next anxious comment, Marlee grabbed her around the waist. A vortex swept them up and plopped them down in Carol's kitchen. As Carol wobbled, Marlee's stockings swished. A poof of smoke, another vortex and

Marlee was gone. Carol's mouth dropped open. The air was empty.

"Phew. I think I need something stronger than this water," Carol said.

Somehow a calming glass of wine didn't seem appropriate, however. Marlee made Carol realize her daily whine had to change.

Chapter 3
Second Period

Carol stashed her school bag under the granite island in the kitchen as soon as she heard the garage door open. She, Bob and the kids enjoyed a reflective dinner of macaroni and cheese. Sara shared a story about lunchroom drama. A "friend" pointed out that Sara was the only one among the four girls who didn't have a boyfriend. Sara had defended herself by pointing out her commitment to dance. Carol didn't say anything out loud, but she thought, "That's my girl!"

Timmy told his family the school's elevator key was missing, again. Hopping up the stairs with his crutches made him miss the first 10 minutes of math. "Oh well," he said. "These crutches are my free pass."

Carol shot Bob an eye dart. "Please put that on your honey-do list for Monday. Call the school."

Bob sighed, "Yes, dear. Pass the salt."

After clearing the dishes, Carol took her school bag to the kitchen table. She cracked open the manila folder to correct papers. Too tired, she rested her head on the stack of research papers and dozed off.

A steady beat, like a bouncing basketball, stole Carol's attention and woke her. Ethereal cheers resonated against the walls of her home, ending in a slam dunk thunk. She sensed she wasn't alone. Looking up, she adjusted her glasses. Carol saw the outline take shape. The radiant brown eyes offset by laugh lines at the outer edges were unmistakable. Oh, how she had a crush on that guy.

"Jeff Hunterdon?" she questioned. Her heartbeat picked up, raced. For an instant her mind darted back to room 134/136. She shared that team teaching space with Jeff during her first two years. Well, year and a half.

"Cargo, Cargo. Yeah, it's me. I'm a sort o' Ghost of Teaching Past. Remember the email spam?"

"Jeff, a what?"

"Together we're gonna take a look back. But, listen, we need to get out on the road," coaxed Jeff as he allowed the basketball he held to roll off to the floor. "You know how to read the map, kiddo." He took her hand and it eerily meshed into hers. For an instant she experienced a warm pins and needles sensation, like a nano electrical shock. Jeff pulled her up from the chair, and their feet no longer touched the floor. Together they left her home kitchen ... through the window.

"Yeah, I know how to read a map when we're in a CAR. Uh, whoa! How are we moving like this?" She searched left, right, above and...below. It already registered that her feet were not touching the ground, but now she and Jeff were somehow moving at a fast clip toward the second floor window...uh-oh, next the slate rooftop of her neighbor's house. "Jeff?"

"Let's just go with it, Cargo." They swooshed over the chimney and several others, a scene reminiscent of Wendy and Peter Pan. Carol scanned her memory, questioning her decision about Jamie Ardiente's happy hour offer. In no time she and Jeff soared above the roads of the entire town, everything below looking like those satellite Mapquest views. Then, head on, she spotted the unique clouds. Or was it nocturnal skywriting? A written message:

"Live as if you were to die tomorrow. Learn as if you were to live forever." Ghandi

Once her brain interpreted the letters, she and Jeff swirled through the cloud mist, descending. Not a window this time. They squeezed through the brick.

"Check it out, Cargo." He hopped up on a desk in the back corner of the room, inviting her to do the same. She nervously stood next to him. A classroom. Something familiar about this one. A retro look and feel. The desks were empty, though. A cart in the back held a Bell and Howell 16mm movie projector.

Jeff snapped his fingers twice as he announced, "Lights, camera." At that, the room dimmed and the clicking of the threaded film through the projector began the search for Carol's past. She stared at the movie screen up front as 21-year-old Carol and student teaching mentor, Matt Golden, came to life.

"That's pretty impressive insight from a student teacher, Miss Goff," Mr. Golden commented in his fatherly way. Carol hadn't heard anyone call her by her maiden name in years. "Back in August, I read your letter of introduction with that Ghandi quote. I knew you were eager to begin your student teaching assignment then, but today's lesson was outta here. You, Miss Goff, had the kids energized, begging for more!" he said, shooting his victory fist into the air.

Carol Goff beamed, smiling with a satisfied sense of self. Mr. Golden had inspired her with his "out of the box" teaching methods. Even though she was only a college senior at the time, Carol had known she was fortunate to have been paired up with him. He was a natural with the students, and she had learned tons of teaching tips by observing him. Freedom and choice. He had entrusted both his students and Carol with freedom and choice in their pursuit of learning. Question. Experiment with your ideas. That had been his mantra. That day Carol wove all the elements together. The tapestry of this social studies lesson: the bombing of Hiroshima. Future lessons: a prepared debate and a point of view Role-Audience-Format-Topic – RAFT – writing activity. She had investigated writing techniques.

Carol further explored, "What if I added a twist to RAFT? Explode a moment to slow it down. Show the reader details, building tension and suspense."

"You're talking like an experienced educator! Trust your instincts," encouraged her mentor.

The verve in that movie scene enveloped Carol Cosgroe. She put her hand on her heart, sighed. Shifting on one foot, Carol leaned over to Jeff, "I haven't sensed that spirit of excitement about a lesson for a long time."

"We're here to tap into it, sort this thing out, Cargo," coached Jeff. As he squeezed her hand, she felt that pins and needles sensation again.

Observing Golden and her younger self, Carol recalled that he had influenced her lessons, constantly espousing the need to incorporate writing into the content areas. He had been ahead of his time, a master of this practice, a novel concept to Carol at the time. College teacher preparation touched on none of this. Carol witnessed how writing to learn - authentic writing - solidified social studies in student minds. This flashback made her realize she had to open her rusty teaching box and sharpen her tools.

The movie followed Carol and her mentor heading toward the door to go to lunch, when Golden began, "Listen, Carol, my wife wants to have a last barbeque of the season Saturday evening to celebrate this Indian summer. Come on over. She's invited Jean from the math department and Frank, the guy who teaches special ed."

Even though the weather had been uncharacteristically hot and humid, the ease of summer seemed distant. Knowing all the work she had to prepare for Monday's college observation, easygoing Carol hesitated a moment. She had a date on Friday night, an aerobics class Saturday morning, and a community outreach commitment with her sorority in the afternoon. Still, she wanted to be with her new colleagues and enjoy some down time.

Golden asked, "Why don't you join us? We can celebrate your great achievement here today. All work and no ... well you gotta have a balance, Carol."

There was all day Sunday, she reasoned, and she had already drafted a skeleton plan for Monday's lesson.

"Sure, I love a cookout. I'm looking forward to a fun time," Carol heard herself respond, and they left for lunch.

In the back of the room, Jeff softly acknowledged, "That's the Cargo I know."

Her heart sank. Could it dive any further? Where had Carol Goff gone?

"Cargo, she's still there inside," Jeff said, having read her thoughts. "C'mon. Let's have a look at the second reel. Oh, I forgot. Now it's time for the VCR. Remember when we were the first team to get a VCR? Our story gets better."

Carol sat down. She knew the setting of this video even better than Golden's room. As the camera zoomed inside, Carol spotted her younger self and a younger Jeff in room 134/136. She caught her breath.

The blackboard showed it was Tuesday, and the afternoon prep period had finally arrived. "Hey, Hunterdon, I have this idea of a spring culminating project for the Mexico unit and wondered if you'd be into combining some social studies with a math class or two," the young Carol announced and questioned all at once.

A twenty- something Jeff looked up from the extended tail of a Hershey wrapper, swallowed and said, "Sure, kiddo, what'll it be?"

"Well, our kids will hold a Mexican market and sell stuff," she began.

"So, this is a money thing? The seventh graders are way past working with money, Cargo." Rubbing his thumb and index fingers along the sides of his chin, he added, "There might be a few in period three who could use a refresher!"

Carol nodded, but clarified her idea, "Not counting money. Instead, you'd help the kids reinforce the economics of the market. Talk about overhead, pricing their items to gain a profit, finally calculating a true profit."

"We could develop a graph based on profits by various items sold and compare the class periods. Or maybe we could graph profits by location of their business. Oh, yeah, I have some ideas marinating in the ol' brain. Definitely. In math, this is the real deal," Jeff said, warming to the project.

It's what Carol counted on: Jeff would jump right in and support this idea and even bring his own extension to the project. Hunterdon was a team player and he loved "playing" with the kids. No yards of notes or miles of films for Hunterdon. At 6'2", he was an overgrown seventh grader in some ways, but in others, Jeff was like a combination of Mr. Golden and musician Bryan Adams. Three years her elder, Jeff was dating outside of school. So was Carol, but she secretly had a huge crush on Jeff, a former basketball player. At the end of her first year, Carol had pondered what would happen if she might act on that crush.

She remembered Golden's mantra: "Experiment with your ideas." Carol took Jeff's lead in the graphing extension proposal. "Hunterdon, I think I'm gonna work to connect writing to this project, too."

"Yeah, Cargo. That interdisciplinary planning really gets the kids going. Maybe I'll come up with a few thoughts of my own to run by you!"

The dismissal buzz. A calendar page rustled on the side bulletin board, altering the scene. Jeff moved off the desk and stood beside her in anticipation. Carol noticed a quick wince as he pushed another tape in the VCR.

"Scene three, Cargo. This one's a roller coaster."

In a montage scene, Carol watched the two of them work together, developing a close relationship. They managed the writing paperwork load together. They used the die-cut machine together. They sang together in the talent show and caroled shoulder-to-shoulder at holiday faculty parties. They high-fived winning points in the faculty-student volleyball games. They were the T in Team!

"That made the teaching fun," Carol mused in the back of the room.

Close-up of Jeff's Apartment 3-B door. He slid the key in the door, turned and opened it. While Jeff ordered dinner, Carol cleared off the coffee table to make room for student folders. She moved the books, two trophies, and a miniature blue, yellow, and red flag to the shelves.

She admired the framed photos of Jeff beside a basketball team, Jeff and family, and autographed 8 x 10's of Michael Jordan and Scottie Pippin. On closer inspection, she noticed several accounting titles and Spanish books. An opened envelope remained on top of two videos on the table alongside a typed correspondence. Some fancy company lettering.

Carol couldn't fend off her curiosity, so she picked up the envelope. She read the return address that said, "The International School in Bogota, Colombia." She turned her head toward the flag on the shelf.

"Pizza will be here in twenty minutes," Jeff said as he re-entered the living room. She averted her eyes from the letter. Jeff had noticed her looking at the coffee table and asked, "What's wrong? Oh, let me get rid of this." He scooped up the mail, shelving it.

They ate pizza, avoiding grease stains on student essays. When the finished pile toppled over, Jeff said he wanted to tell her some really great news. She figured it was about the basketball team he coached.

Eyes fixated on the classroom movie screen, Carol Cosgroe's face told that she knew differently. Her memory warned that the "roller coaster" was heading for a lurch, leading to a spiral descent. She leaned forward, her hands cupped together, nervously rotating around one another.

Back on the screen, Jeff sat upright on the sofa, explaining to Carol Goff that during the summer he had applied to the International School in Colombia. He wanted to continue to do what he loved while seeing that country. Today he got a letter offering him a teaching position in Bogota. He applied for next school year, but they wanted him this January. It was an opportunity he intended to snatch up.

This came out of nowhere. He never mentioned it at school. Carol wanted to be excited for him, but her heart couldn't connect. Tears spilled from her eyes.

Seeing Carol's reaction, Jeff said, "I know the timing

isn't great. I'm sure the district will get a good replacement."

Carol dropped her glance, shaking her head no. Red blotches grew on her neck.

"I'm filling one of three available positions. Maybe they need a social studies teacher. If you come with me, it'll be a real adventure. We work great together, Cargo."

Carol watched her younger self say, "You're leaving? How long has this been in the works? I just can't leave my life here. Colombia isn't an apartment complex away."

The VCR suddenly stopped and ejected the tape. The slow illumination of the room revealed a pained look on Carol Cosgroe's face.

Jeff leaned in and spoke in a soft, clear voice. "Cargo, I really wanted you to take that leap and come along to Colombia, but it was *my* dream. My words to you made it seem so easy to do. I didn't think about what you'd have to give up. I knew how upset you were that night. Back then, I guess I just didn't expect you to write me off, ignore my calls, skip school my last day, never answer my letters."

"I couldn't wrap my head around it, Jeff. I felt abandoned that night. Even before you actually left. Later it didn't help that your replacement was so ornery and difficult. I asked for a transfer that June." Carol crossed her arms over her chest and shrugged. "Now that I think about it, maybe that's when teaching started to change for me. You quit the team and I felt abandoned."

"This can't take away the past and make everything all right, but I am here to apologize," Jeff said. "I'm sorry. We came on this trip tonight so you could remember the awesome teacher you are. And so I could repair the damage I may have caused."

After an uncomfortable silence, Carol added, "Take me home."

Jeff and Carol ascended the evening sky in a quick

swirl. En route to her house, Jeff broke the silence to explain she would be visited by other ghosts.

"Who next?"

"Not sure, Cargo. Wait and see."

At that the two of them squeezed through the mist and back to her kitchen table. He bounced his basketball and touched her arm. Carol pushed away his hand and glared at him. A poof of smoke, a vortex and Jeff disappeared. Carol let out a deep sigh.

Chapter 4
Third Period

Carol lifted her head off the kitchen table and wiped dribble from her chin. The microwave beeped and a basketball wobbled in the middle of the floor. She picked up the basketball and pressed the timer off, noticing only ten minutes passed since Bob and the kids left. How could any of this be real? She blamed it on the chicken lo mein leftovers she gulped down for lunch.

Her clogs clip-clopped as she trod down the hallway toward the basement. She would just put away the basketball herself. Her house was so quiet, so peaceful. So different than school. Fluorescent yellow light leaked from underneath the basement door, so Carol sighed and pulled it open. She muttered as she clomped down the rickety stairs. Just as she turned the corner at the bottom, she gasped and the basketball fell from the crook of her arm. A barrel-chested, hairy man in surfer shorts and a Hawaiian shirt stood before her. His gray hair flopped over his eyes and his luminous smile revealed a gap between his shiny front teeth. Carol thought he looked familiar but couldn't place him.

Behind him, the ping pong table was filled with pineapples, a roasted pig, complete with apple in its mouth, hamburgers, hot dogs and more. The coconut sunblock smell reminded her of the beach.

"Oh, just come on. I don't need an Evite. Marlee and Jeff told you to expect me," he said with his hands on his hips.

Carol backed up toward the stairs.

"Carol - remember Tiger Pride?"

She detected a trace of a Russian accent in his voice.

"Mr. Alexandrovich? Is that you?"

"As sure as the beets in my grandma's borscht!"

That small expression took Carol back to meetings with her all-time favorite principal, who retired to Hawaii.

He motioned toward a set of rainbow striped sand chairs. "Carol, your skepticism always was your light and your shadow. It makes you a wonderful social scientist and has turned you into probably the most un-fun human being on the East Coast."

"Wh---whaaaa---what do you mean? Un-fun? I---I---am a houseful of fun!"

Mr. Alexandrovich crossed his arms over his hairy chest and stared.

"I-I-I wore a sombrero for Hat Day. That was fun."

His seashell anklet jangled as he shook his foot. "My toes are tingling with excitement. Sit down. Now."

She plopped into the chair with a crack of her knees and a sigh. The mountain of a man with the familiar twinkling green eyes sat next to her. He set a surfboard across their laps and tapped it. "Hold onto Betty."

Carol did as she was told and VRR-ROOOOOOOOOOOOOOOOM. She hung onto Mr. Alexandrovich's Hawaiian shirt as they surfed over smoky chimneys, children sledding down gently sloping hills, cars meandering through slush. Icicles hung from eaves and snow piled up on sides of driveways.

He took a sharp turn, the subdivisions replaced with narrow alleys and rickety clotheslines.

"Where are we going?" asked Carol as she pulled her jacket tighter.

"Come on," he whispered and drew Carol toward a brick building. Despite the bleak exterior, the interior of the apartment glowed. Family photos lined book shelves and end tables. The steady bum---bum-bum of Spanish dance music traveled through the air along with the smell of fried food. A crocheted afghan draped over the back of a worn sofa lined with pillows embroidered with *World's Best Mom* and *Family Is Forever*.

A petite woman wearing meticulously ironed scrubs

shouted, "OK, Janissa! Make sure you get Xenia to bed by 8 p.m."

"OK, Mami." A teen in a gray hoodie and pink pajama bottoms hugged the woman before sitting next to the baby's highchair.

"Janissa," whispered Carol, hands on her hips, watching the scene unfold. "She never does her homework and mostly sleeps through class."

"Carol," admonished Mr. Alexandrovich as he patted her back, "patience, please."

Carol crossed her arms over her chest and leaned against the stranger's refrigerator. She noticed a magnet that said, "We might not have it all together, but together we have it all."

The baby squinched her eyes and moved her head away from Janissa as soon as the spoonful of fruit puree touched her lips. "Oh boy, Xenia, this is going to be one of those nights," said Janissa. She kissed her little sister on the cheek.

Their mom patted Janissa on her head. "Thanks for taking such good care of your sister. Hopefully I can get off the 7p-7a shift at the hospital soon." She kissed baby Xenia and said, "You be good for your big sister, understand?" The baby giggled and slapped her tiny fists on the high chair tray, sending rice puffs flying to the floor.

Carol and Mr. Alexandrovich watched Janissa feed her sister, give her a bottle and put her to bed. Janissa washed the dishes and swept the floor. Only then did she pick up her school bag.

Carol stared at the girl and said, "She actually does her homework!" She tiptoed over to the table and peeked over Janissa's shoulder at her agenda book.

❤ *Draft of How to Be Poem for science (volcano)*
Algebra p. 56-57, #2-46 even
Read for 20 minutes and do reading log (vampire book!!!!)
Social studies ?????

Carol gasped. "Oh my God! Really? We spent ten minutes going over the homework, a compare contrast paragraph about the British and the colonists at the Boston Massacre! Do I need an air horn? Sky writing? These kids today!"

"Carol," whispered the ghost. "Take a chill pill. What period do you have this child?"

"First." Carol, arms still across her chest, sneered, "So what if she's tired? She listed all of the other teachers' homework. I put my heart and soul into my classes and work hard for these kids."

The ghost rolled his eyes.

Janissa plowed through her homework. Giggling, she wrote the final line of her volcano How To Be Poem: "Don't forget that poisonous gases can come from volcanoes' ashes!"

Carol surprised herself by giggling, too. "Although that's not FACTUALLY correct. The gases come before the ashes. OK, I admit it. THAT is pretty funny. I KNOW Ardiente is going to eat that up!"

"Whoa. That's the smile I remember!" announced Mr. Alexandrovich, his hands spread wide.

"Like I said earlier, I wore a sombrero for Hat Day. I know how to have a good time."

The spirit rolled his eyes again, plopped on the sofa and patted the cushion next to him. "Come on, Cosgroe. Speaking of fun, Ol' Betty has somewhere else to take you."

Headlights twinkled below the pair as they jettisoned higher and zipped through snowflakes. They coasted above the river, following its meandering path through the valley. Soon the lights of the mall glimmered below. With a whoomph, they landed in Fezziwig's Tavern.

Carol heard a familiar noise that steamrolled into a belly laugh. There huddled Jamie Ardiente and a bunch of their colleagues, as promised, enjoying appletinis and beers. Their laugh-a-thon swelled to such side-hugging, tear-wiping, red-faced mirth that it prompted Carol to say, "I wish I knew what was so funny."

"Scout's honor, she LITERALLY said, 'bah, humbug' to me!" A snort punctuated Jamie's sentence and the group sputtered into more laughter.

Carol recalled their conversation that afternoon about TGIF plans. Her eyes narrowed. "Why ... she ... she's making fun of me! Shame on her, all I do for her!"

Through a mouthful of peanuts, Mr. Alexandrovich asked, "What exactly do you do for her?"

"Plenty. I tell her the inside scoop on who's who and what's what. I remind her of deadlines. We made sure her teacher induction binder was in order."

"Plenty. Hmmm. Isn't she the one who brought you homemade chicken noodle soup for lunch when you had that cold in November? And isn't she the one who always drops your mail off in the morning so you don't have to trek to the office? Doesn't she leave you Hershey's Kisses on your desk sometimes? Doesn't she invite you to every conference and class she takes?" the ghost asked.

"She'll grow out of that. Naiveté of youth."

Another teacher in the booth wagged a finger and said, "'Walk! Walk! Walk!' I hear Cosgroe screaming that down the hallway in my dreams!"

"I don't scream...." Carol whispered.

Jamie jumped in again. "Now, come on. We all have our idiosyncrasies now and then."

A gym teacher Carol knew to be very quiet and shy bellowed, "Idiosyncrasies? That's ONE way to put it! Cosgroe scares the beejesus out of me. The way she complains in staff meetings-she's the first to complain but never offers a solution. I have no patience for her. That's why I don't talk around her."

The happy hour conversation threaded in and out of topics like work, relationships, books and work again. Jamie talked about her newest project idea. "So, OK, guys. Here's what I'm doin' with my eighth graders. We're going to do multigenre research projects."

"Multiwhooziewhatsies?" asked a math teacher as she texted someone.

"Multigenre research projects. The kids will pick a topic, like maybe hurricanes. Maybe they'll construct a 3D timeline of important U.S. hurricanes or write a poem about the creation and categories on the Saffir-Simpson Hurricane Scale. The possibilities are endless for our kids to learn AND showcase their creativity at the same time," Jamie explained. "Now, let's get this pitcher refilled. Sorry. That's enough shop talk."

Carol turned to Mr. Alexandrovich. "I have to give it to Jamie. She has that new teacher glow, believes all things are possible. She'll be back to five paragraph essays in no time. She'll learn."

The spirit pushed his bangs out of his face and said, "I remember when you believed all things were possible. YOU were the one who gave ME energy on those rough days. Kept me from jumping on the first plane back to Moscow."

Jamie poured a round of beers. She raised her glass and said, "Let's all make a toast to Carol. May she come out and join us someday soon and forgive us our merriment at her expense!"

WOOOOOOOOOOOOSH and Carol and Mr. Alexandrovich were soaring back above roofs and streetlights. This time, the snowflakes flittered into letters that read, "Keep Calm and Carry On."

The windows of County General Hospital glowed and the pair surfed into a room filled with laughing children. A few men sat in folding chairs, each with two children nestled in their laps. One man held up a copy of *Olivia* and read it with such charm and gusto that even the teenagers in the room were rapt. Carol recognized someone.

"That's LeSean Thomas," Carol said. "He did one of the best projects on the First Amendment I've ever seen. His parents even took him to the National Archives in Washington, D.C. to see the original Constitution."

A little boy in a hospital gown cuddled against LeSean,

his skinny legs swinging back and forth. The pair laughed along with the others in the room as he hugged him tight.

Carol and Mr. Alexandrovich flew over a dismal street jammed with liquor stores, check cashing stores and pawn shops. Lights glimmered brightly in a social hall where an old man with thick glasses croaked, "BINGO!" The dozen or so octogenarians clapped when someone verified his numbers and gave him a brand new electric blanket as his prize. A group of teenagers wheeled out carts of donuts and hot drinks. Carol blinked and recognized the flame red hair and green eyes of one of the teenagers.

"Hey, Kevin was one of the funniest students I've ever had. Seems he's found something to do with all that charm," said Carol.

"I remember him," said Mr. Alexandrovich. "He took first place in one of the talent shows!"

A sweet, little old lady warbled, "home, home on the range," and soon, the crowd joined in the chorus.

Again, Mr. Alexandrovich sped on, this time to a gymnasium, where men and women in their desert fatigues matched rucksacks against a checklist. Some talked on their phones or organized their carry-ons. Soldiers joked and gave each other hi-fives. A banner from Carol's student council hung on the walls, declaring, "We Love Our American Heroes."

"Did I ever get to sign it?" Carol wondered aloud as she searched for her signature.

Just as quickly as they entered, the pair left, coasting between the stars and the streetlamps.

"Boy, Mr. Alexandrovich, now I can see why kids don't meet deadlines on my school projects. The stuff they deal with after 3 p.m. and on the weekends is much more life and death. Yet, I am inspired. They find joy and laughter in such dismal places," Carol said.

Old Betty hovered above the roof, dipped and glided through the patio door. The pair materialized on the staircase. The silence was deafening.

The ghost pointed to Sara's room. Tears flowed down her daughter's cheeks as she wrote in a journal. Carol wanted to hug her daughter. Instead, she found herself in the basement, where Timmy sat on the sofa, his broken leg propped up on the ottoman. The flickering T.V. cast a ghostly light on her firstborn.

She heard duct tape being ripped off cardboard boxes and Bob muttering to himself as he sorted the contents between a garbage bag and a Rubbermaid tote. He aimed a dart at the Honey Do list hanging on the wall and yelled, "Bullseye!"

Carol's husband held up a tarnished trophy with a man and a woman dancing. He shined the name plate with the hem of his T-shirt and smiled as he read aloud, "Bob and Carol Cosgroe Tango Champions 1997." He placed it into the rubber container but paused and jammed it into a bulging trash bag. Carol watched him drag the black bag from the patio door to the curb along with the other garbage.

Suddenly, Carol's cell phone vibrated. Carol dabbed perspiration from her forehead. Caller ID read, "Unknown." Carol accepted anyway. On the other end, a gong echoed, tremulous and deep. Children's voices whispered behind the resonating boom, but it soon shriveled and the whispers took over. Carol pressed the phone to her ear. The voices called, "Isolation ... want ... isolation ... want ... isolation ... want ... isolation ... want ..."

Carol gasped. She threw the phone and realized Mr. Alexandrovich was gone. She now stood in her basement with the light humming above her head. On the memo board next to the laundry room door, a dry-erase marker jumped to life and penned, "The only way to make sense out of change is to plunge into it, move with it, and enjoy the dance."

Carol sighed. "Let me rethink that glass of wine." She trudged up the stairs, wondering what awaited her next.

Chapter 5
Fourth Period

Back at the kitchen table, Carol wondered, "Why is this night so different from other nights?" Ghosts aside, she was still sitting with her red pen and student papers. She'd promised Bob she'd be good to herself.

Carol stepped away from the table, sat in lotus position on the floor, legs crossed, fingers touching and practiced her yoga breathing. "Inhale, look for the positive. Exhale, put that red pen away. Inhale, breathe in the fresh air of opportunity. Exhale, stop complaining. Inhale, exhale." With a last cleansing breath, Carol decided to go upstairs and change into her softest pajamas and *Life is Good* socks. She adjusted her pillows, climbed into bed and started to read Sara's latest edition of *People.*

The magazine slipped from her grasp. She was awakened by a soft touch. Carol opened her eyes and thought she saw Jamie Ardiente appear from a haze. Carol muttered, "Oy vey. So *she's* the last ghost."

Jamie sat on the edge of the bed and queried in a mellow voice, "What made you decide to become a teacher?"

Carol was confused. "Aren't you at Fezziwig's Pub?"

Jamie responded,

"At Fezziwig's Pub you thought I'd be
But you mean so much more to me
Your struggles came through loud this day
I'm here to help you find your way."

Carol rubbed her eyes, blinked twice and said, "OK, let's get the show on the road."

Jamie repeated, "Think about what made you become a teacher. Those visions are the breadcrumbs to help you find your purpose."

Carol listened and thought, "My purpose. What is my purpose?" Her eyes welled up.

Jamie gently touched her hand. "Remember, sometimes crying is silent but cleansing, Carol." Jamie took Carol by the hand and they levitated toward the ceiling and out the window.

As they flew across the fresh crisp snow, a large forest came into view. Carol smiled at Jamie and remarked, "Nothing calms me like the peaceful serenity of a forest." Frost's words came alive and Carol said, "Two roads diverged in a yellow wood." In the moonlight Carol read a small sign nestled between two snow covered pines. Etched in the wood it said, "Carol, Teacher of the Future." Two arrows pointed in opposite directions.

"Which path do you want to take?" Jamie asked. "Both lay snowy and want wear."

The road to the left looked straight. A teacher sat at a flawlessly organized desk, her pencils perfectly and evenly sharpened. Pens were arranged by color in the pretty Pampered Chef organizer. The file cabinet was meticulous, with color coordinated, evenly stuffed and alphabetized folders. This teacher resembled Carol. Though perfectly groomed and dressed in a starched white blouse with black pants and flat shoes, her funky hair was gone. The simply dressed woman matched the decor, plain, clean, no excess. All the students wrote their assignments neatly in their agenda books. Everyone mechanically followed the rules. There were no characters: No Emilys, no Janissas, no LeSeans. All was quiet. A Mark Twain quote popped into a speech bubble, "*Truth is stranger than fiction. But it is because fiction is obliged to stick to the possibilities. Truth isn't.*" Carol wondered, "Is this path my truth?"

The road on the right wound through a snowy bank. Carol squinted, trying to grasp a glimpse of the next setting. This looked clearly different: Engaged students wrote, read and talked in small groups. Wait ... a smorgasbord of students (Janissa, LeSean, Kevin) lit up that room. A girl resembling Sara wore a T-shirt stating, "Flexible people don't get bent out of shape." Carol smiled. Jumbled pens and pencils littered her desk beside a rock that stated, "All are accepted for who you are … no exceptions." Several students sat in bean bag chairs, books scattered near them. The teacher moved around the room as the guide on the side, not the sage on the stage.

Carol remarked, "Look, I am learning from the kids."

Jamie assured her, "Nice of you to notice. There is a Buddhist saying, 'When the student is ready, the teacher appears.' Keep that thought. You're not even finished reading the room." On the wall were two signs. The first was:

Good Writers …

Observe

Take opportunities to write

Read

Listen to their own writing

Revise

Rewrite

Read like a writer

Make connections

Share

Investigate

The second sign was a certificate from the National Writing Project. Carol Goff Cosgroe's name was on it.

"Writing! Mr. Golden would be so proud!" she exclaimed. "He always thought writing was important no matter what the subject. He taught me the power of writing as a learning tool. How can I learn more?"

Jamie asked, "How can WE learn together? Haven't you learned that isolating yourself isn't working?"

Carol stood up straighter and said, "You know what, I DO want to feel better about teaching, about my ability to impact children, about life. Timing is everything, Ardiente."

Carol and Jamie floated into the mist, then back through Carol's bedroom window. The curtains billowed. Jamie's voice resonated in the soft silent night.

"You've seen the paths
In the whispering woods
Observed the place each teacher stood
Choose the trail to blaze your way
Your future really starts today."

Tucking Carol back into her soft, safe bed, Jamie evaporated into the cool, clear air and Carol fell into a deep, restful sleep.

Chapter 6
Fifth Period

Saturday morning's sun greeted Carol with warm reflection off the fresh, crisp snow. After a quick shower, she slipped into her Penn State sweats and tiptoed out of the house. Carol drove on the freshly cleared roads, parked and walked into the bookstore. Vivaldi played through the surround sound. She sauntered up to the empty café and treated herself to a latte. Tempting as it was, Carol passed on the warm, chewy chocolate croissant. After all, she did have to watch her figure. She settled on a multigrain bagel with butter on the side and filled a box with scones, crumb cake and a carrot cake special to go for her family.

Next, a book hunt. She remembered a Mark Twain quote, "The difference between the right word and the nearly right word is the difference between light and a lightening bug." She needed some light to lift her out of her doldrums.

As Carol sauntered down the aisles, she suddenly heard a familiar voice.

"Morning, Carol. Nice to see you here. It's nice to see there is life outside of school, right?"

Carol responded, "So they say, Eliza. Nice to see you."

"What brings you out so early?" asked Eliza Stewart as she bent down to tie her running shoes.

"I'm looking for something to read over the holiday weekend," Carol replied.

"Me, too," said Eliza, holding up a book called, *Teaching Writing in the Content Areas.* "I'm reading this book this weekend to get ready for the conference I'm going to next Saturday."

"What conference is that?" Carol asked.

"Penn State Lehigh Valley Writing Project's Best Practices Conference. It's an annual event and it always recharges my batteries to get through the second half of the school year."

Carol stood up straighter. She tilted her head, widened her eyes and put her hand on her hip. "Hmmm. Did you say recharge your batteries? Is it really worth giving up a Saturday?"

"Absolutely," Eliza said. "Remember I told you a long time ago, I'm a National Writing Project Fellow. I do some leadership work with the Penn State site. I still say becoming a member and going through the Summer Institute is the best six graduate credits I ever got. And I've got plenty more graduate credits than that."

"Really?" Carol practically sang. She stared out over the book shelves. "So this is what it means that the teacher appears when the student is ready."

"What?" Eliza asked.

"Never mind. Where can I get more information about this conference?"

"Go to LVWP.org. You can sign up right there."

"Awesome!" Carol said. "I will do that. Boy, I'm glad I ran into you." Looking at her watch, Carol said, "As you can see, I was busy making my family's breakfast this morning. The toughest part was getting the treats into this pretty box. Thanks for the chat. I'll see you Tuesday."

"OK. You got it," Eliza said. "See you."

Carol hummed *I'm A Believer* as she made her way to the checkout and quickly purchased the book, the newspaper, an aqua gel pen and the latest edition of *People* magazine for Sara.

On the drive home, Carol phoned Bob. "Don't eat breakfast. I'm bringing it home. I think I'll take the scenic route, so see you in 10 minutes." She turned on the radio and *Eye of the Tiger*, by Survivor, pulsed out of the speakers.

When she pulled into the driveway, Carol saw the garbage sitting at the curb. She parked, ran into the house and handed Bob the box of pastries. "I'll be right back," she told him.

Carol jogged down the driveway. She dug through two trash bags and piles of slimy banana peels, coffee grounds and other assorted, unidentifiable gunk, before she found it. Her breath steamed in the cold, morning air as she wiped off the dancing competition trophy with the sleeve of her sweatshirt. She sprinted back into the house, rinsed it off and set it on the mantle.

"Went the distance, now I'm back on my feet, just a gal and the will to survive!" she sang to no one as she set the table. "Come and get it. Breakfast is ready!" she called.

Timmy thumped down the stairs in his cast. At the table he said, "Morning, Mom. What's all this? Are you OK? You're pretty happy this morning."

"Yes, well, life is good," she said. "I'm just grateful."

Timmy shrugged and sat down.

Sara walked into the kitchen with dark circles under her eyes. Carol hugged her and said, "I have a bit of work to do, then how about you and I go for pedicures? Here's the newest *People* magazine to hold you over."

"Thanks, Mom," Sara said, exchanging glances with Timmy. "What's got into you?"

Carol just smiled and asked, "Where's Dad? He was here a few minutes ago."

Bob clumped up the basement stairs. Carol ran to the mantle and grabbed the trophy. "I don't really want to throw this away. Don't you forget, I'm your trophy wife!"

Bob laughed out loud. "Sounds like somebody had a good night's sleep."

After breakfast, Carol set the laptop on the kitchen table. She googled www.lvwp.org. Several snippets launched from the site:

"I came away with confidence, new ideas and a strong support system."

"I used a broader range of learning opportunities."

"It provided an opportunity to improve writing for all learners."

Out loud, Carol said, "I'm signing up for the conference. This looks like good stuff."

She opened her Outlook and wrote an email to Jamie. "I decided to go to this conference. Please join me. Here's the link."

Carol also decided it was time to take back her Saturdays. The essays, the grades, the lesson plans could wait. She wanted to enjoy time with her family. She wanted to relax a little. It was a three-day weekend anyway.

***

Tuesday began with a faculty meeting and Carol took her usual spot at the back of the library, in the closest seat to the door. Her colleagues filed by, carrying travel mugs and Dunkin Donuts bags. She nodded "hi" to the few colleagues who acknowledged her. Instead of playing Words with Friends on her iPhone during the meeting, Carol actually listened. After the assistant principal, Ms. Sharpe, shared a guided reading of the school's calendar events, Carol raised her hand to speak.

Sharpe's eyebrows shot up as she said, "Ummm - yes, Carol?"

Carol noticed Jamie staring at her. She saw the gym teacher who said she was afraid of her shift in her seat. Carol cleared her throat. "Well, I see we already have a problem with this calendar."

Her colleagues glanced at their shoes, tapped their pencils, shuffled through papers, looked at their watches, doodled. Anything to block out what was sure to be another complaint from Cranky Cosgroe.

"Well," Carol began, her voice stern. She pushed her trifocals to the tip of her nose. "It seems to me that we have scheduled time for testing, tutoring, Family Math Night and all of these other activities. Years ago, when I was younger," Carol continued, noticing Jamie biting her lip. "We had a talent show."

Her colleagues' heads rose from their paperwork and

clock watching. Carol sensed their eyes on her. Jamie leaned in.

Carol continued, "I think it's high time we have some fun with a capital F around here. If it's OK with administration, I'd like to form a committee to bring back the Spring Showcase. I've recently been reminded that there's more to our students than their grades."

Sharpe cocked her head and smiled. "Well, OK, Carol. Get a group of people together and draw up a proposal."

Carol looked around the room and didn't expect to see any hands pop up immediately. She noticed teachers exchanging glances and even heard a few "hmmms" in the crowd. She felt relieved when Jamie gave her a thumbs-up.

After dismissal, Carol headed home. She heaved her schoolbag onto the granite island in the kitchen and opened her manila folder of student work. She grabbed the new aqua pen. "I need to search for what's right with my students," Carol said aloud. "I will look at them with fresh eyes."

She placed the rubric with the writing prompts in front of her. The paper read:

1. What have you learned about war?
2. How do you view yourself in a changing world?
3. Based upon the historical events we have studied, if you could create a bumper sticker of inspiration, what would it be?

For the next two hours, Carol looked over the responses. She sighed from time to time. She was even moved to exclaim, "Wow, this one's really good!" three times. When she got through the stack of papers, she set the notable three on top. "These are the ones I'll share with my classes tomorrow. Maybe Ardiente can teach me how to use that darn document camera, too."

Before she packed everything away for the night, she read the standouts again.

Madelyn had written, "When you look inside a person and see her heart, that is when you see who the person really is."

Michael, aka I Am Camo Man, had written, "I like guns. I like the glory. But now I have to rethink my dream. After studying the war with Mrs. Cosgroe, I learned the price was different. People really die in war."

Janissa had written, "Hope is when you wait for the perfect moment to come."

***

Appendix
Lesson Plans

Lesson: When Life Gives You Lemons, Make Lemonade

Objective:
Students will write narrative memoir stories about a time they experienced troubles and how they overcame them. They will narrow their topics and pay particular attention to craft (sentence fluency, word choice and voice).

PA Standards: Types of Writing and Quality of Writing; Speaking and Listening
This assignment can be adapted and used in conjunction with books read or topics of discussion, as appropriate, in Language Arts; English; Psychology; Social Studies or Science. (In Science, for example, it could be used in conjunction with a mechanical sciences unit in which students must invent solutions to problems.)

Common Core Writing Standard Grades 6-12:
Write narratives to develop real or imagined experiences or events using effective technique, well-chosen details, and well-structured event sequences.

Instructions:
- Class discussion of idiom, "When life gives you lemons, make lemonade."

- Discuss world-renowned phenomenon about Alex's Lemonade Stand and show a couple videos:
  Volvo for Live, Alexandra Scott:
  http://www.youtube.com/watch?v=K2gZafuF_TU
  Alexandra Scott, Alex's Lemonade Stand:
  http://www.youtube.com/watch?v=QWCrb_q8s_U

- Brainstorm story ideas. Discuss concept of voice and writing from the heart.

- During pre-writing, students will narrow their topic and outline it according to the 5Ws (Who, What, When, Where, Why, How) and 6 Senses (See, Hear, Smell, Taste, Touch, Feel emotions).

- Students will write first draft, revise and edit.

- Motivation to continue – a cup of lemonade and a lemon poppyseed muffin for sustenance

- Possible mini-lessons – narrow the topic; introduction, middle, conclusion; vocabulary, empty/excess words (word choice); voice; passive verbs; revision; editing.

Resources:
- Write Traits handout

- Teacher tip sheets for introductions, conclusions, vocabulary, passive verbs, voice, revision, editing, etc.

Lesson: Tall Tales

Objective:
Students will write original narrative tall tale stories to develop written and oral story telling skills. They will narrow their topics and pay particular attention to craft (sentence fluency, word choice and voice, especially use of idioms).

PA Standards: Types of Writing and Quality of Writing; Speaking and Listening

Common Core Writing Standard Grades 6-12:
Write narratives to develop real or imagined experiences or events using effective technique, well-chosen details, and well-structured event sequences.

Instructions:
- Class discussion of what constitutes a tall tale (a lie), as opposed to other types of tales, including folk tales, fairy tales, science fiction tales, fantasy, legends. (See checklist below of story elements for beginning, middle and end.)

- Read portions of *Whoppers, Tall Tales and Other Lies*, by Alvin Schwartz (J.B. Lippincott Company, NY, 1975), especially the first 20 pages.

- You can also read Dr. Seuss stories.

- You may find current stories in tabloids.

- Discuss idioms. Useful resource: *Scholastic Dictionary of Idioms* by Marvin Terban.

- Share a teacher-written story, especially effective as a model!

- During pre-writing, students will narrow their topic and outline it according to the 5Ws (Who, What, When, Where, Why, How) and 6 Senses (See, Hear, Smell, Taste, Touch, Feel emotions).

- Students will write first draft, revise and edit.

Resources:

- Write Traits handout
- Tall Tales Checklist
- Teacher created List of Idioms

Tall Tale Checklist

✓ 1 = 5Ws introduction

Ideas and content: __ real people names
          __ real places
          __ real situations
          __ real numbers and facts

✓ 2 = Transition – Stretch the truth with Exaggeration (Hyperbole)

Ideas and content: __ far-fetched situations and events
          __ ridiculous names of people and/
            or places
          __ BIG numbers

✓ 3 = Conclusion

Ideas and content: __ Explains what happened at the end
          __ Includes one of the following at
            the end (or something similar):

* I know it's true (or I know it happened) because I was there…

* My aunt (or someone else) can tell you it really happened because she was there, but she had to go out of town…

Overall:

Word choice: __ specific nouns
          __ active, lively verbs
          __ limited passive verbs
          __ appropriately placed idioms

Conventions: __ spelling, capitals, punctuation, past tense verbs

The Write Traits

Ideas and Content

It all makes sense.
I know this topic well.
I have included interesting details not everyone would think of.

My paper has a purpose.
Once you start reading, you will not want to stop.

Organization

Piece starts off with a bang.
Everything ties together.
It builds to the good parts.
You can follow it easily from beginning to middle to end.

At the end it feels finished and makes you think.

Voice

This really sounds like me, like my personality.
It uses my kind of expressions.
My reader can tell that I care about this topic.
This is what I think (my opinion).

I express my emotion.

It is easy to read aloud.

Word Choice

This is the best way to say this.

I can picture it!

My words are new ways to say everyday things.

I have included powerful verbs.

Some of the words linger in my mind.

It is easy to read aloud.

Sentence Fluency

My sentences begin in different ways.

Some sentences are short and some are long.

It just sounds good as I read it because punctuation tells me where to pause and add emphasis.

My sentences have power and punch.

Conventions

I don't have grammar mistakes in my paper.

I have used capitals correctly.

Periods, commas, exclamation points and quotation marks are in the right places.

Every word is spelled correctly.

Verb tenses are correct and consistent (all present, all past, etc.)

Comparing Write Traits to PA State Domains

6 Write Traits	4 PA Domains
Ideas and Content	Focus
Organization	Organization
Voice	Style = Voice, SF, WC
Sentence Fluency (SF)	
Word Choice (WC)	
Conventions	Conventions

Project Outline: Multigenre Research Project

Objective:
Students will teach their classmates about a topic through transforming research into mini-projects of varying genres.

PA Standards: Writing 1.4.8.B: Write multi-paragraph informational pieces (e.g. letters, descriptions, reports, instructions, essays, articles, interviews)
Use relevant graphics (e.g. maps, charts, graphs, tables, illustrations, photographs)
Use primary and secondary sources, as appropriate to task.

Common Core Writing Standard Grades 6-12:
Write informative/explanatory texts to examine and convey complex ideas and information clearly and accurately through the effective selection, organization, and analysis of content.

Resources:
Blending Genre, Altering Style: Writing Multigenre Papers by Tom Romano

My students really like this example of an MGRP done as a novel study: http://www.users.muohio.edu/romanots/pdf/bloodandbravery.pdf

http://www.heinemann.com/shared/onlineresources/E00785/chapter1.pdf

Instructions:
Part 1: Introduction and Topic Exploration
Unpack the meaning of "multigenre." Show students examples (see resources section).

This depends on the course you are teaching and will work in ANY content area. It's a nice way of extending knowledge in any discipline. As an English language arts teacher, I have my students do a lot of prewriting (see below) about classes they enjoy and what they'd want to learn more about.

Part 2: Project Planning/Initial Research

Provide a graphic organizer to help students identify their main topic and the subtopics they will research and present. For each subtopic, leave space for students to identify the genre through which they will convey their learning. For example:

Poem	Song	Advertisement
Short story	Musical Composi-	Radio report
Scene	tion	Website
Screenplay	Dance	Debate
News report	Monologue	Collage
Power Point Presen-	Poster	CD cover
tation	Brochure	MP3 song playlist
Twitter feeds	Greeting Card	Scuplture
Facebook page	Map	Painting
Prezi	Interview	Drawing
Poster	Editorial	Design a piece of
Article	Obituary	clothing
Timeline	Birth Announce-	
Journal Entry	ment	

This is a good time to distribute the rubric so students know what they're working toward.

Part 3: Research

Give students time to research topics, making sure they are staying focused on each subtopic only.

Part 4: Drafting

I suggest setting deadlines for drafts of each subtopic. It will give you an idea of where they are going with their learning and will also give students time to see what their classmates are doing. This time to self-calibrate is crucial for successful final drafts.

Part 5: Planning For Final Drafts

A to-do graphic organizer is very helpful in this stage. There will be many things to consider and modeling how to stay organized is invaluable.

Part 6: Presentations

Provide PLENTY of time for students to share and celebrate their learning. Leave time for their classmates to ask questions.

Lesson: Explode a Moment

Objective:
Students will add detail description to a significant event in their writing in order to slow down time, causing the reader to more fully experience the event.

PA Standards: Types of Writing and Quality of Writing; Speaking and Listening

Common Core Writing Standard Grades 6-12:
Develop and strengthen writing as needed by planning, revising, editing, rewriting, or trying a new approach.

Instructions:
- Discuss the use of slow motion in the film industry and reasons the director makes a decision to use it. Point out that it can increase the sense of drama/tension the audience feels.

- Show a video clip from a familiar movie or the ultraslo website which gives an example of slow motion.

- Discuss the effect the slow segment has on the story line and the audience.

- Tell students that to slow a moment in their writing, they can imagine themselves in that position and use their senses to describe in words what was seen, felt, heard, etc.

- Read an example of this type of writing from a picture book or novel. Guide students through locating the words and phrases that do the work of explosion.

- Together try a revision of an event that begs for this writing strategy, eliciting ideas from the group. Display the two versions side by side.

- Ask students to find an area in their piece that would be enhanced through the use of exploding that moment. Independently have them revise those sections to share

Resources:

Barry Lane's book, *The Revisor's Toolbox,* has a section on Explode a Moment.

www.ultraslo.com

Lesson: RAFT (Role-Audience-Format-Topic) Writing Strategy

Objectives:

Students will produce a written piece in the content area after choosing the point of view, the audience to whom they are writing, a format, and the topic.

PA Standards: Types of Writing and Quality of Writing; Speaking and Listening

Common Core Writing Standard Grades 6-12:

Write informative/explanatory texts to examine and convey complex ideas and information clearly and accurately through the effective selection, organization, and analysis of content.

Instructions:

- Explain to students that they will write a piece based on a recently studied topic and that each student will use the RAFT strategy as their guide.

- Reveal the words each letter in RAFT represents. Give example choices for each, similar to the following RAFT choices regarding a Social Studies lesson about the bombing of Hiroshima:

    Role - the Enola Gay; grown child of a Japanese survivor; J. Robert Oppenheimer; U.S. ambassador to Japan

    Audience - a group of nuclear physicists; a Japanese middle school class;, a book publisher; a WWII veteran

    Format - a postcard; memoir; poem; a speech

    Topic - Bombing of Hiroshima; the need to regulate weapon creation; an apology; health and psychological effects of the atom bomb; an account of the day

- As a class, create and record a RAFT together, using teacher choices.

- Create another RAFT, but allow the class to make role choices, etc. for everyone to use.

- Have small groups collaborate and draft the piece they'll share.

- Finally, students use the RAFT strategy on their own, to write an individually created piece.

Resources
www.writingfix.com has ideas for each aspect of RAFT

"Picture Book RAFTs for the Social Sciences" by Doug Fisher and Nancy Frey San Diego State University

Lesson: Writing and Designing Postcards: A Virtual Trip

Objectives:

- Students will take notes from at least two resources about their topic

- Students will cite resources using a template

- Students will write a postcard using information and stating 3 places they visited on their virtual trip.

- Students will design a postcard that will visually describe their visit by using technology and/or art supplies.

PA Standards:

Information Literacy Standards

- The student accesses information efficiently and effectively.

- The student pursues information related to personal interest.

- The student creates information in different formats.

- The student uses information responsibly.

Pennsylvania Academic Standards for Reading and Writing

- 1.4 Types of Writing B; informational piece using illustrations when relevant.

- 1.5 E Quality of writing; Edit writing using conventions of writing.

Common Core Writing Standard:

Write informative/explanatory texts to examine and convey complex ideas and information clearly and accurately through the effective selection, organization, and analysis of content.

Prerequisite Skill Level:
- Note taking using 4 square

- Using a works cited template for books, encyclopedias and/or websites

- Reading and writing

- Use of written address in proper format

- Ability to write a friendly letter

Materials:
- 4 square note taking paper

- Works cited template

- Final Copy oak tag (5"x8")

- Globe

- Rubric

Resources:
An Armadillo From Amarillo by Lynne Cherry

Around the World, Who's Been Here by Lindsay Barrett George

Introduction
1. Using a globe and *Around the World, Who's Been Here,* the teacher will introduce the postcard project by showing examples of student work. Student engagement will include sharing an interesting fact at each port. (Example-Panda Bears live in China).
2. Students will have the opportunity to research a place of interest and pair share an idea prior to writing.

Writing
1. Students will generate a list of places and activities they could visit on their trip.
2. Students will set up headings on their 4 square

Places to visit	Natural Resources
Food	Interesting Facts

3. Notes will be taken in bulleted form.

4. Students will complete writing a draft by using their notes.

Evaluation

- Rubric (see below)

- Conferencing

- Works Cited

- Self reflection:

> The best part of my trip was….
>
> I loved the research because…..
>
> Another place I would love to visit is…..because….

Differentiation

- Travel brochure

- PowerPoint Presentation

- Poster Creation

- Cross Curricular Applications

  > Animal habitats- science

  > Foreign language.

For top scores

Includes more than 3 interesting facts

Address is written without errors

Card is attractive, states the place and is creative

Student worked independently

No grammar, punctuation or spelling errors

Lesson: Enhancing Vocabulary and Writing through Picture Books

Objective:
Students will determine or clarify the meaning of unknown and multiple-meaning word and phrased based on grade 3 (or appropriate grade level) reading and content, choosing flexibility from a range of strategies.

Standards:
Information Literacy
Creates information in different formats.

PA Reading & Writing Standards
- 1.3 Read and respond to literature
- 1.4 Writing for different purposes
- 1.5 Quality of writing

Common Core Writing Standard Grades 6-12:
Write narratives to develop real or imagined experiences or events using effective technique, well-chosen details, and well-structured event sequences.

Instruction:
1. The students will listen to *The Tale of the Mandarin Ducks* by Newbery award author Katherine Paterson (*Bridge to Terabithia & Jacob Have I Loved*) and illustrated by Caldecott Award winning illustrators Leo and Diane Dillon (*Why Mosquitoes Buzz in Peoples' Ears*)
2. **Engagement Strategy**: The students will listen to the story and write down spicy writing and/or vocabulary in their journals. As the teacher reads the story, she will ask students to identify a spicy word and define it. (See student generated list attached).

   a. Students will write a story that begins with "Long ago and far away" and use a prescribed number of new vocabulary words.

b. Students will sit in a circle on the floor with their journals. The teacher will ask them to identify the setting of the story (in the forest). Using one sense at a time, students will write a sentence describing the forest. After each writing opportunity for each sense, everyone will share their writing. Extra attention will be made to using **similes, alliteration, onomatopoeia, personification, multiple adjectives,** etc.

    i.   *I **hear** the chirping birds*
    ii. *I **feel** the embracing breath of calm, quiet nature*
    iii. *I **taste** gooey chewy marshmallows.*
    iv. *I **smell** Merry Christmas*
    v. *I **see** the chipmunk rattling in the leafy tree.*

3. **Extension:** Students will have the opportunity to select a place to visit using their own senses and write about them. Samples may include:

- Park

- Mountains

- Cruise

- Plane ride

- Amusement park

- Library

- Snorkeling

- Etc.

4. **Closure:** Students will critique each other's writing in a pair share.

a. Something fabulous I noticed was:
b. Could you tell me more about?
c. Students will share their revisions.

Third Grade Vocabulary from Library

abolish
ailing
annoyance
blended
brocade
capital punishment
captivity
cast
commanded
commotion
compassion
crested
darted
delicacies
desired
determined
distance
ghostly
gleaming

grieving
humiliated
impenetrable
merciful
mightiest
moat
mourning
plumage
rapidly
rustle
scarlet
scavenged
shrine
stumble
trembling
typhoon
weary
whipped

Works Cited

Books

Author: _____

Title _____

Publisher _____

Copyright _____

Author _____

Title _____

Publisher _____

Copyright _____

Encyclopedias

Article _____

Encyclopedia _____

Copyright _____

Article _____

Encyclopedia _____

Copyright _____

Websites

Article _____

URL: _____

Date Accessed _____

Article _____

URL: _____

Date Accessed _____

Article _____

URL: _____

Date Accessed _____

Questions for *A Teacher, Carol*

1. Why/how did you decide to write an adaptation of *A Christmas Carol?*

Ricki: We knew we needed a structure that would allow us to divide and conquer. *A Christmas Carol* is divided into four sections. Just what we needed!

Heather: Ricki wanted to write fiction and I was trying to think of ways to make it happen with four people writing the book. Fiction writing is hard enough for one person! I wondered if we could pick a story we already knew and adapt it. I've always been a fan of the *Christmas Carol* adaptations, like *Scrooged* and *A Diva's Christmas Carol* and thought it could work.

Vicky: Heather had the idea and she was the fiction expert among us. There was absolute sense to using the template to give structure to our writing.

Audrey: This was my first formal fiction writing experience. I remember meeting Ricki and Heather at a local book store café and purchased *A Christmas Carol.* Believe it or not, I could not remember reading it. Not being a lover of the 'supernatural,' this was a stretch for me.

2. The book sounds like it was written by one author. Explain the writing process.

Ricki: Each author wrote her section on her own and posted it on a wiki. As we looked at each other's writing, it became easier to pick up a consistent style. We did give each other feedback about sentence length and chapter length and we each went back to rewrite and reduce! We had to rework some of the writing in collaboration to make the style flow. We developed Carol and Jamie's looks first by working with prompts on a graphic organizer. I based another character on a former colleague and good friend. It helped to have a picture of a real person in my head.

Heather: One thing we had to do was iron out the details about Carol - who is she? What does she want? What are her conflicts? Everything else flowed around that. We had to create characters that would highlight her and challenge her. We also decided that Carol's last name would be a pronounceable anagram of Scrooge in order to have some fun with language.

Vicky: Ricki had given us tips based on the book, *Growing Great Characters from the Ground Up,* by Martha Engber. That helped me. Ricki, our taskmaster, continually aided us and prompted us with structural support.

Audrey: This part of our process provided the glue for our group. Each of us had a passion for our own chapter. We asked many questions regarding the character's motivation, clarity of the plot. Although it was initially a challenge for four people to write a book, the gift was being supportive, respectful, critical friends to keep the integrity and the heart of the book.

3. How did technology play a role in the production of your book?

Ricki: Technology is great when it works! We started with a wiki to collaborate from our separate houses. When we got together, we worked with Google Docs. It was very slow. Sometimes we would be typing like mad and the words wouldn't show up until minutes later!

Heather: I relied on my iTunes, Pandora and Spotify to get me through my drafting. My writing always needs a soundtrack. Also, everyone was open to the wiki and using Google Docs. Without collaborative writing tools (which we learned about at LVWP workshops), this project would have been impossible.

Vicky: Technology was our method of communication when we weren't meeting to work together. I learned more about technology by using wiki spaces, Google Docs. In the past I wrote a first draft by hand then transferred work to the computer. This book was completely computerized for me.

Audrey: We were communicating and sharing with a click of the mouse. The speed and quality of communication were enhanced. It was a learning experience and Heather is very patient.

4. Where, when and how did you write?

Ricki: I wrote on my laptop at my work table in my living room. When it was time to work face-to-face, we met mostly at my house on the Granite Island. Once the three other women got the hang of facing their cars all in the same direction on the u-shaped driveway, it was smooth sailing! Once in the summer we went on a retreat and wrote at Audrey's Pocono lake house. The most important part was that we set dates on the calendar and stuck to them. Incorporating sustenance was very important.

Heather: When I had to write on my own, I wrote in our office or on the sofa. Summer vacation was such a luxury for this project because I could write whenever my muse knocked on my brain, including 3 a.m., if I wanted. When school was in session, I had to schedule writing time and be very disciplined about keeping to that schedule. We also gave ourselves a word count limit for our sections, so it helped us stay in check and balanced.

Vicky: Most of the writing was done on my computer during the summer ... thank goodness for that time to think. Ideas easily flowed. I wrote in my living room as I sat in an overstuffed chair. Almost all collaborative revision came about at Ricki's kitchen Granite Island, except a meeting we had at Audrey's peaceful lake home.

Audrey: We drafted on our own, starting with Word and attachments, proceeded to the wiki and Google Docs. I clearly remember the moment when we said, "Carol would never say that!" Our characters took on a life of their own.

5. Writers say, "Start the characters." Did you find that the characters helped tell the story?

Ricki: I taught creative writing for several years. I kept remembering the tips I told my students about how to develop characters. I had never done it myself! We referred to the tutorial sheets I made for my students (from extensive research about how novelists develop characters).

Heather: We got to a point where we started asking each other, "What would Carol do here?" or "What would Jamie be wearing?" We were able to talk about the characters in terms of people, which made us stay honest to their personalities and history.

Vicky: Our writing posts occurred at various times and I found it helpful to read over each coauthor's post to keep Carol consistent.

Audrey: We literally traveled back in time. What was showing at the movies then? What did we wear? What music was playing? Some of us had to travel "farther" than others.

6. Can you identify any best practices you utilized or developed?

Ricki: Cooperative learning was the most important best practice we utilized. It was good to tell students we were writing a book because that kept the pressure on me the way I put the pressure on them!

Heather: We made sure to focus on what we were doing well and repeated it. We couched our suggestions for revision sincerely and carefully.

Vicky: I took Ricki's suggestion and just plunked the ideas on the computer when I wrote the rough drafts. I didn't revise anything the same day; I came back later to do that work.

Audrey: The power of revision was multifaceted. We wrote independently, revised, wrote, revised and then worked as a supportive group and questioned each other, "Did you want to say this, that or something else?" There is an intimacy that develops when you birth a book together.

7. How do you think each person's background impacted the development of your story?

Ricki: Some of us are more concise, just-the-facts writers and some of us are more voice-flowery. I still write journalism style on a daily basis as Community Relations Coordinator and television news teacher. I appreciated the flowery additions from the others!

Heather: We each teach different grade levels and subjects, so we were able to pull from a broad range of experiences and topics. Our different personality styles also influenced how our story developed.

Vicky: I knew from the beginning that we were each coming from different facets of the education and writing fields. It was a gourmet recipe for writing. Ricki's newspaper experience kept us focused, working on deadlines and, well, just focused. I looked to Heather as the fiction specialist and her work with other fiction writers often impacted our book decisions as she questioned us and lent her experience. Audrey's knowledge of literature permeated the work while her fascination with words drove the word choice.

Audrey: In addition to our different professional experiences, our personal strengths helped us get to the finish line: Ricki- the taskmaster; Heather- the techno geek; Vicky, the diplomat; and I- the researcher.

8. If you had to give any advice regarding collaborative writing, what would it be?

Ricki: Consider all ideas thoroughly before deciding to incorporate or reject. You must listen with open heart and mind and not take things personally. This was advice we gave each other, not necessarily getting it from an outside source.

Heather: It's helpful to have a collaborative partner who owns a house at a lake or has a gigantic kitchen with a lovely granite island. Locations aside, once you commit to meeting dates, stick with them. Keep an open mind and relax. Everyone's strengths will come into play in different, beautiful ways.

Vicky: Laughter ... you'll need it! Respect. Not all of us knew one another before we gathered, though there were common threads. Everyone worked hard and respected each other's ideas and abilities.

Audrey: Positive reinforcement, diplomatic questioning, lots of food, good sense of humor.

9. Most people find writing is a solitary activity. What were the benefits of writing as a group? Would you do it again?

Ricki: I started two books previously. I co-wrote the first one, finished it and let the co-author publish it. The second one is fiction and only 50 pages so far. I needed a group to give me confidence and the pressure to finish. This experience has been very satisfying. I look forward to working with the group on the sequel.

Heather: My weaknesses were their strengths. When I was stuck, they unstuck me. When I was blah, they made me laugh. I would do it again for sure. I can't wait to see where we go with the sequel.

Vicky: Camaraderie! And learning personal writing process from one another was insightful. The motivation was there to produce quality work on time for meetings. YES, I would repeat this experience.

Audrey: I would do it again, because my writing, teaching, collaboration skills and friendships were strengthened. I modeled the questioning techniques our writing group used with my students.

10. What is one word to describe this experience?

Ricki: Productive.

Heather: Affirming.

Vicky: Fulfilling.

Audrey: Enlightening.

About the Authors

(We wanted to make you a snazzy Venn diagram but, alas, it would have taken us longer than to write the book. We hit a few technology snags. Watch for improved technology skills in our next book!)

Erica (Ricki) Stein transitioned from a 15-year career as a newspaper sportswriter to teaching. She thought she would know how to teach children to write. When her students' writing disappointed her, she enrolled in the Penn State Lehigh Valley Writing Project Summer Institute in 1995. She learned to write with voice, which she has modeled for students ever since. Several of her suburban students have written novels. Ricki currently teaches students to write through television news and writes as her district's Community Relations Coordinator.

Heather Harlen teaches 8th grade English in an urban school district. She began her career as a Peace Corps volunteer in Russia and has also taught in adult ESL and alternative education programs. Along with her secondary English teaching certificate, she holds an M.A. in creative writing and a B.A. in English. In 2004, she participated in the Penn State Lehigh Valley Writing Project's Summer Institute, where she learned the best way to learn as a teacher is through the wisdom of other teachers.

Vicky Lynott was invigorated in 2004 when she attended the Penn State Lehigh Valley Writing Project Summer Institute. It offered the middle school veteran a sense of freedom and choice, a pack of fireworks, for her role of teacher as writer. Now in her 30th year, she tells her students, "When you begin with a plan and put pencil to paper, you never know exactly where it will take you." This is her second book.

Audrey Alexander Nolte has been a classroom teacher, adjunct instructor, workshop presenter and school library media specialist. Her passion for connecting literature, writing, storytelling, and life-long learning through the curriculum energizes student focused learning. She became a National Writing Fellow through the Penn State- Lehigh Valley site in 2010. The NWP awakened her love of vocabulary development through reading and writing. Audrey works as a library coordinator and writing coach in a suburban school district.

To contact the authors visit www.lvwp.org.